To Pe[...]
I wish [...]
very best in your
new school
froom
Tom   21/7/95

Beningfield's English Farm

Beningfield's English Farm

GORDON BENINGFIELD

VIKING

VIKING

Penguin Books Ltd, Harmondsworth, Middlesex, England
Viking Penguin Inc., 40 West 23rd Street, New York, New York 10010, U.S.A.
Penguin Books Australia Ltd, Ringwood, Victoria, Australia
Penguin Books Canada Ltd, 2801 John Street, Markham, Ontario, Canada
Penguin Books (N.Z.) Ltd, 182-190 Wairau Road, Auckland 10, New Zealand

First published 1988
Copyright © Gordon Beningfield (pictures) and Cameron Books 1988

Edited and designed by Ian Cameron
Produced by Cameron Books, 2a Roman Way, London N7 8XG

Filmset in Linotype Times by Cameron Books
Colour photography by Cameron Books
Reproduced and printed in Holland by Royal Smeets Offset, Weert

British Library Cataloguing in Publication Data available

ISBN 0-670-81191-2

Gordon Beningfield is grateful to all the various people and organisations who have provided
him with facilities and help during the preparation of this book. Particular thanks are due to
Mr and Mrs Joe Henson of the Cotswold Farm Park, to the Weald & Downland Museum,
Wimpole Home Farm and the Longford Children's Farm, St Margarets, Hertfordshire.

This book is a celebration of the English mixed farm and its animals. As most of the English countryside is farmed, its fate is inseparable from the future of farming. My whole life has been coloured by memories of the traditional farms that I knew as a boy, more than forty years ago. The mixed farm, which has since been laid waste by the financial attractions of intensive production coupled with rich subsidies, was founded on a degree of respect for the countryside that came from having to co-exist with nature. How different is 'modern' farming which sets out to bludgeon nature into submission by waging chemical warfare on anything that gets in the way of profit and imprisoning its livestock so that nature becomes an irrelevance. What I have tried to evoke in this book is an attitude to farming and farm animals that makes very good sense to me, but seems to be largely a thing of the past.

Contents

The following books on farm livestock have been consulted during the compilation of the text. I am indebted to them for a large amount of factual information.

Lawrence Alderson *The Chance to Survive* Cameron & Tayleur/David & Charles, 1978
Lawrence Alderson *The Observer's Book of Farm Animals* Warne, 1976
Frank Townend Barton *Cattle, Sheep and Pigs* Jarrold, 1912
Herman Biddell *et al Heavy Horses. Breeds and Management* Vinton, 1919 edition
Edward Brown *Races of Domestic Poultry* Edward Arnold, 1906
H. Clausen & E.J. Ipsen *Farm Animals in Colour* Blandford, 1970
David Low *On the Domesticated Animals of the British Islands* Longman, 1845 edition
H.S. Holmes Pegler *The Book of the Goat* The Bazaar, Exchange and Mart, 1917 edition
Robert Trow-Smith *A History of British Livestock Husbandry 1700-1900* Routledge, 1959
J.F.H. Thomas *Sheep* Faber, 1944
Derek Wallis *The Rare Breeds Handbook* Blandford, 1986
John Wrightson *Sheep. Breeds and Management* Vinton, 1895

The Oldest Breed

Of all the British breeds of farm livestock, the White Park can probably claim to be the oldest. White, horned cattle may have come to Britain with the Romans over 2,000 years ago. Quite possibly, though, they were introduced by the Beaker people who arrived nearly 2,000 years before the Roman invasion of 55 BC. Whichever theory is correct, the white cattle were reared as sacrificial beasts for religious rituals, whether by the Romans or by the Druids. It is not difficult to imagine the mystical significance that could have been attributed to a magnificent, pure white bull.

The White Park bulls in my pictures are show animals from occasions such as the Rare Breeds Survival Trust's annual show and sale. The man in the drawing on the next page had to be modified to look more as I felt he should rather than being dressed like something out of *Starsky and Hutch*. Today, the White Park has become popular in farm parks, more for its beauty than for its long history.

In the Dark Ages, after the departure of the Romans, the white cattle became wild, much in the way that the descendants of domesticated goats have formed feral populations in some of the more rugged parts of Britain. The wild white cattle, along with the other larger inhabitants of the forests that covered much of the country, were hunted by the Norman barons after the Conquest of 1066. At the height of their power, under the Plantagenets in the thirteeenth century, some of the barons were granted the right to enclose areas of forest as parks for hunting. Chillingham Park, near Alnwick in Northumberland, was created in the reign of Henry III (1216-72) and still houses a herd of wild white cattle that humans approach at their peril.

Other herds of wild white cattle that were enclosed in baronial hunting parks at around the same time were the ancestors of today's White Park cattle, which are very similar to the Chillingham herd apart from usually having black rather than red ears. At some point, probably in the sixteenth century, they were tamed, and in the nineteenth century the bullocks of at least one herd were used as draught animals to pull carts and ploughs. Although the British government has little record of helping to save breeds from extinction, it did see the White Park as enough of a national treasure to order a herd to be shipped across the Atlantic in 1940 to ensure that the breed would not get wiped out in the event of a German invasion, and the herd is still in existence on the King Ranch in Texas.

Before the advent of farm parks, where the beauty of these animals has put them much in demand, White Park cattle were extremely rare,

surviving only in a few herds, including three that date back to the thirteenth century. Their numbers are still small, perhaps 200 cows, but increasing. Like at least some of the 23 breeds of livestock that have become extinct in Britain this century, the White Park has characteristics that are worth preserving: the bulls are said to be valuable as sires of beef cattle, particularly now that lean meat is in demand, and the breed also appears to be resistant to some bovine diseases such as pneumonia. In a changing world, who can tell what other characteristics will be of value in the future? There is more than sentiment and aesthetic appeal behind the preservation of breeds like the White Park.

This White Park bull was in a small stockyard that has been lovingly
reconstructed at the Weald and Downland Museum at Singleton in Sussex,
using post and rail fencing and a timber-framed, peg-tiled shed open along
one side.

Traditional Scenes

The biggest problem in painting a bookful of pictures of the traditional English farm and its animals is finding the settings. Even the rarest of the surviving breeds can be seen in farm parks, but traditional farm buildings, where they have not been converted into desirable country residences for commuting yuppies, have fallen into disuse and decay. Wood, brick, stone and tile have been replaced by concrete, metal and plastic. The chequerboard pattern of small fields separated by abundant hedges has been replaced over much of southern England by open prairies divided at most by barbed wire.

A scene that I well remember from the wartime days when I was a boy
helping around the farm: wooden buildings with peg-tiled roofs and cows
standing in the farm pond. In this case, the buildings still exist, but I have
had to imagine the cattle standing there.

Another scene from my childhood: the river Ver in Hertfordshire. It is towards the end of winter, one of those days when you think that at last spring is on the way.

A mare of the sort that might have pulled a trap, here with her foal: a
traditional country scene.

In the traditional countryside, every field had its gate, not a tubular metal contraption, but a proper wooden gate, which might well have been made locally and blended into the landscape. The gates that I have to go through as I search for subjects to paint have often been kept in service for many years only by the sort of improvisation that is one of the farmworker's natural talents. Here, wood from the hedgerow has been used to fill the gaps between the gatepost and the nearest small tree.

These scenes of harvesting are inspired by wartime memories of farming in Hertfordshire which have been refreshed by my visits to Holme-on-Spalding-Moor in Yorkshire where there is a farm that still uses horse power rather than tractors. In these pictures, the sheaves are being loaded on a wagon to be taken and used for building ricks. This was a commonplace sight around my home right through the 1940s.

This picture started with my seeing a Shire horse pulling an Oxfordshire wagon across the show ground in Peterborough during the Heavy Horse Show. Again, the sight triggered memories of the war years. I have transposed the horse and wagon into a landscape that I remember. It is the end of the day in the harvest field. Work has been going on since the early morning: shifting stooks of corn for rick building. Now the horse and wagon are going home, but they will be back again tomorrow to finish the job. As they depart, the geese come out from the farmyard to glean.

Ducks around a farm pond, a study for a larger painting of the Silver Appleyard ducks that I have sketched in pencil. The others are two of the varieties that were commonest when a pond with a few ducks was a usual part of the farmyard: the Aylesbury and the Khaki Campbell.

A Sussex landscape, based on the Weald and Downland Museum, where they farm in traditional ways. Fifty years ago, this would have been seen as a timeless scene that could have been found over much of southern England for a century or more. It is only since the war that the drastic changes brought about by the mechanisation of farming have changed the face of the countryside, often almost beyond recognition.

A Hertfordshire farm that has kept many of its traditional features, including post-and-rail and picket fencing and wooden gates, all of which are shown in the picture. The gate, which might have been made by a local carpenter, was obviously put together from wood that was not very well seasoned, so that it has twisted and turned a bit, gaining a character of its own. The little building is a grain store, the survivor of two that the farm used to have. It has weather-boarded and heavily tarred walls and a peg-tiled roof lined with lead. The saddle stones on which it stands help to keep out the damp and make it a little more difficult for the rats and mice to get in.

A Sussex downland sheep farm with its barns and the sheep being driven out for grazing from the barnyard where they are kept.

Southdown sheep with a shepherd's hut based on the one that I own. One of the sheep is wearing a canister bell. Being the smallest of the downland breeds, the Southdown is light enough not to break up the turf with its hooves, and so is ideal for the Downs. Strangely enough, there are many more Southdowns abroad than there are in Britain, where only about 1,500 remain. The qualities of the breed were so renowned that it was exported to Australia and New Zealand, to the Americas and to continental Europe. As one expert put it, 'No breed of sheep in the whole world equals the Southdown as a producer of the highest grade of mutton.' For every Southdown in its native Sussex, there are several hundred on the slopes of the Massif Central in France.

A Sussex landscape preserved at the Weald and Downland Museum: a thatched barn with ricks behind and typical Sussex post and rail fencing in the foreground.

Donkeys are often put into the same field as horses to keep them company and be their friends. The animals for this scene, which could be on a mixed farm anywhere in southern England, were from the Cotswold Farm Park. The donkeys with the lovely Shire horse are shedding their coats, which are hanging off in places.

The Belted Galloway, so-called because of the striking white belt around the otherwise black or dun-coloured body, originated in southwestern Scotland. These animals are part of a herd that is owned by the Boxmoor Trust in Hertfordshire.

Longhorns

Two hundred years ago, the Longhorn was supreme among cattle, the only breed that was to be seen throughout the length and breadth of England. The experts of the time believed that it had originated in Lancashire, and it was first improved – the polite word for making it more commercial – in the adjoining Craven area of the West Riding of Yorkshire. The Craven Longhorn was a triple-purpose beast, a source of milk and beef as well as being a draught animal. By the time it had been further improved, first by a Mr Webster of Canley, near Coventry, and then by the most famous breeder of all, Robert Bakewell of Dishley Grange, near Loughborough in Leicestershire, the Longhorn had become a very different creature.

Today's Longhorns, which are lean and long in the body, are a far cry from Bakewell's creation. As a commercial breeder, he went straight for the quality he wanted at the expense of all others. What he wanted was to produce the maximum amount of meat, no matter how fatty, as quickly as possible to satisfy the demand from the rapidly expanding population of the towns in the early days of the Industrial Revolution.

'He aimed,' wrote David Low in the 1840s, 'at producing the large cylindrical body, in all the animals destined to be fattened, and a smallness of the head, neck, and extremities, or what is called fineness of bone. A saying of his, often quoted, is, that "all was useless that was not beef;" . . . He adopted, too, the homely profit-and-loss maxim of breeding the animals large in the parts which are of most value to be sold; and hence, in his breed of cattle, he made the shoulders comparatively small, and the hind-quarters proportionally large.'

The result was a very fatty barrel on legs, and, according to Low, the cows were 'eminently deficient in their power of yielding milk.' No wonder, then, as Low said, 'its reputation has passed away, even more quickly than it was acquired.' By the beginning of the nineteenth century, it had been pushed out of fashion by the Shorthorn breed, which was developed by Charles and Robert Colling of Darlington. The Durham Ox, son of one of the Collings's bulls, weighed some 3,000 pounds and spent six years travelling around in a caravan to be exhibited to astonished country folk.

Another reason for the downfall of the Longhorn was its impressive horns, which were inconvenient in a draught animal and limited the density with which they could be stocked in yards. It is ironic that the horns have contributed to the breed's survival in recent years by making it spectacular enough to be a big attraction in farm parks. Its commercial appeal today is exactly the opposite of Bakewell's ideal: the breed is valued for its leanness.

Longhorns are so wonderfully docile that I was able to go right up to a cow with a calf and stroke her. Still, you have to be careful because of the horns. A gentle Longhorn cow might want to swing round and scratch her back, taking you with her.

Producing calves is something that Longhorns are very good at, particularly in comparison with some of the continental breeds that it has been fashionable to import. The economic advantages of the fast-growing Charolais are more than compensated for by the easier birth and better survival rate of Longhorn calves.

I love their variety of horns: no two animals seem to have them exactly the same shape. Their colour can be anything from dark brown to brindled mixtures of chestnut, grey and cream – there is no feeling of computerised uniformity about Longhorns. Usually they have rather heavy coats, which animals that mainly lived outdoors would have needed. The Longhorns in these pictures were at Wimpole Home Farm, near Royston in Hertfordshire, which is run by the National Trust as a traditional farm with old breeds that the public can see and enjoy. The only change I have made to the setting is to change the roof from slate to tile, purely for the colour. Even the Bantams were actually there, pecking around.

This fine, well-preserved timber-framed barn belongs to the large Georgian farmhouse you can see in the background. Barns like this one, which must be well over a hundred years old, are usually listed as buildings of architectural importance, but that often does not seem to be sufficient protection. Either they mysteriously get knocked down or they're left to go to rack and ruin, and simply fall down.

Gloucester Cattle

The Gloucester is the rarest of all English breeds of cattle, and has always been largely restricted to its native county and neighbouring parts of Somerset and Wiltshire. It is said that the richness of the milk and the small size of the fat globules it contained made Gloucester milk ideal for cheese-making. This was the milk that was made into the original Double Gloucester cheese. When the Gloucester Cattle Society was formed in 1973, only 58 cows and heifers remained. There were only three bloodlines among the bulls, and those could hardly be called pure, as Shorthorn, Welsh Black, White Park and Friesian blood have been introduced into the Gloucester stock at various times during the twentieth century.

The distinguishing feature of the Gloucester is its colouring, which varies from a deep, rich chestnut to almost black with a white stripe running along the back, including the tail and extending down under the belly. I saw this magnificent bull at the Cotswold Farm Park in Gloucestershire, which has a herd of this breed. I added the stile, and either the bull is daring you to come over it or you are thanking your luck at having got over in time.

In this painting of Gloucesters in an imaginary setting of watermeadows, I have aimed to capture some of the feeling of a nineteenth-century animal portrait, which seems appropriate for these cattle of the past (but, I hope, of the future as well). The black bull is a very powerful creature obviously interested in the young brown cow but also aware of the other cattle that seem to be walking away across the river.

A Dorset Farm

When it came up for auction in 1987, Lower Kingcombe Farm in Dorset had remained unspoilt for hundreds of years. It was then a race against time to keep the place out of the hands of developers or unsympathetic farmers. Thanks to a tremendous campaign by the Dorset Trust for Nature Conservation and its friends, which brought big contributions from celebrities as well as a multitude of tiny ones from ordinary people in south-west Dorset, £200,000 was raised within a fortnight, and most of the farm was saved for posterity. The whole episode was very encouraging as a further reminder that, given publicity, the destroyers of the countryside can no longer rely on people's apathy.

A corner of the meadows at Lower Kingcombe in late autumn, with the leaves virtually gone from the trees. It is early morning with a heavy dew almost turning to frost because of the chill in the air. A slight mist is lifting to give that weak, pale lemon sunlight that is typical of the time of year. The fencing is made with boughs from the hedgerows. This scene, happily, is not imaginary, but it represents the aspect of the traditional farm that is much harder to find than the animals.

The sketch shows Lower Kingcombe early in the year, looking across the river Hook to one of the meadows that will produce abundant, sweet-smelling hay in the summer and where the wild flowers that have been exterminated over the swathes of improved prairie still flourish. In the foreground, on the river bank, are water irises, and there is another of the fences made of pieces of wood taken from the hedgerows and therefore a bit higgledy-piggledy rather than mechanical and straight.

A typical example at Lower Kingcombe of English agricultural land as it used to be, with hedgerows, beech trees and a rough track going off into the next meadow.

There are some places to which I return year after year. One of them is the Dorset village of Powerstock. In the area are two flocks of Dorset Horn sheep, some of which I have painted here in the traditional setting of a deep, leafy coombe. The Dorset Horn is descended from the old tan-faced sheep of the area with perhaps some contribution from the Spanish Merino, a breed that was fashionable in the early nineteenth century but entirely unsuited to the English climate. Dorset sheep have been renowned for hundreds of years for their ability, unique among British breeds, to lamb twice a year, and particularly to produce lambs in October when other sheep are being mated – a valuable quality in the days before refrigeration.

Tucked away in the coombes of Dorset there are still many small, family farms. On this one, a rick of straw has virtually collapsed – you can still see the remains of thatching on top, and the farmer has propped the rick up with branches. It has become an attraction for the chickens, which have come to scratch about. It is spring, and there is a rookery in the trees behind the rick, which the farmer has still taken the trouble to thatch even though it is made of bales rather than the traditional sheaves.

An imaginary scene with a tip-up tumbril cart and a four-wheeled trailer in the background by a thatched rick. Another of my early memories is of playing on hay ricks and being chased off by the farmer. Sliding down them was great fun, particularly if there was a convenient pile of straw at the bottom, but it was not very good for the thatch.

Round, thatched ricks like these are now very unusual, but you can still find them on small farms in Dorset.

Outdoor Pigs

The history of domesticated pigs is much less well documented than that of cattle, sheep or horses. Although pigs were kept by many farmers and cottagers, they were mainly for home consumption. Two hundred years ago, large-scale pig-keeping happened only where brewing or cheese-making provided a plentiful supply of waste products that could be used as a cheap source of feed to deal with porcine appetites. The animals themselves were descended from the European wild boar and retained many of the characteristics of their ancestor, an active creature that foraged for its living in the forests. In an era when pigs were driven on foot from Norfolk to London, a degree of vigour was clearly an advantage.

This is Fred, a Gloucester Old Spot who is an old friend, though one you have to treat with respect because of his massive size. In its home county, this breed was developed to use up the fallen apples from the cider orchards and the whey from cheese-making. In fact, it used to be known as the orchard pig and has the strong, hairy coat that goes with being hardy enough to live outdoors. Pigs were a common sight in orchards – there used to be a small sty in the orchard behind my cottage, kept by the parents of my neighbour, Mr Fowler, who was well into his nineties when he died recently. I have put Fred and a Gloucester Old Spot sow back in the setting where they belong, with a few geese who are keeping their distance in the backgound.

Some day these hardy, outdoor pigs will come back into fashion, perhaps when oil supplies run out and the real costs of factory farming start to be acknowledged. Then maybe farmers will recognise the thrifty virtues of pigs that can live outdoors, produce piglets efficiently and manage on a diet that does not have to be exquisitely calculated. Another of these breeds is the Tamworth, a long-legged, long-snouted pig that is perfectly capable of getting some of its food by rooting in the woodlands as its ancestors would have done hundreds of years ago. Behind the two Tamworths in the sketch is one of another minority breed, a young Middle White.

The Tamworth is a lovely russet colour, which is said to be the result of interbreeding between English pigs and Red Barbadan pigs from the West Indies. Nevertheless, this breed from Staffordshire has many of the characteristics of the unimproved pigs of two or three centuries ago, and when Joe Henson was trying to reconstitute an approximation to an Iron Age pig, he crossed Tamworth sows with wild boars to produce black and rust coloured animals whose piglets were striped like wild boar piglets. In the picture, you can see the Tamworth's long snout for foraging. Like all the pig breeds in this book, the Tamworth is very rare. In the background is a crossbred Middle White, a great character, who will appear again later in the book.

The Berkshire pig that I found at a little farm in my village is shown in an old-fashioned sty, which is simply a tiny hut with open ends. Behind is a dung clamp with chickens pecking around on it. Later versions of the outdoor sty were made of half hoops of corrugated iron and were quite a common sight on the fields of Hertfordshire. Berkshire pigs were well known in the eighteenth century, but even as late as the 1840s they were still large sandy-coloured animals with black patches and lop ears, very different from today's small fat Berkshire, which is largely black with prick ears. Because pigs reproduce so quickly and prolifically, the breeds can be changed much faster than those of other farm livestock to fit current demand or fashion.

Another victim of fashion is the curiously snub-nosed Middle White, which a year or two ago was down to about a hundred breeding sows, the same sort of level as the Berkshire and the Tamworth. In the 1910s, though, an expert was able to say, 'A cottager cannot go wrong in purchasing one of these pigs . . . A degree of perfection has been attained in the Middle White, and no one has ever been able to produce a better or more useful type of pig.' By 1986, the story had changed completely, and a book on rare breeds stated flatly that the Middle White 'has very little role to play in today's pig industry.'

The Middle White was developed about a hundred years ago as a cross between two other breeds. One was the Large White, which had been evolved as a back-yard pig in the early nineteenth century by weavers and other factory workers in the West Riding of Yorkshire; it is still an extremely popular breed. The other was the Small White, a very fat little pig from which the Middle White took its pushed-in snout and some of its shape. These characteristics in the Small White showed the influence of the wild pig of eastern Asia via Chinese pigs which were introduced into Britain in the late eighteenth century and probably contributed to the make-up of some if not all of our pig breeds. Another eighteenth-century introduction with Asiatic blood in it, the black Neapolitan pig from Italy, was involved in the evolution of the modern Berkshire.

The Small White is now extinct: small, fat pigs were already out of fashion almost eighty years ago, when one writer remarked, 'Very little need be said about the Small White, because the demand is equally small.' Not that the Small White reached the extremes of obesity represented by another extinct breed, the Dorset Gold Tip: 'so forced were these roly-poly pigs that life must have been a burden. To prevent accidents from suffocation, the pigs were supplied with pillows made from round pieces of wood. They were placed by the pigmen under the snouts of the reclining beauties; whilst the effort to walk out of the pens to be examined by the judges was frequently so great that the attempt was often abandoned.'

While such absurd creatures are probably no great loss, another pig that was being backed for success in the 1910s certainly did not deserve extinction: 'It is hardy, a quick feeder, good breeder, attains great weight, and the pork is juicy and of fine texture.' All these qualities were not enough to save the last Lincolnshire Curly Coat pigs from being slaughtered in 1972. It may be difficult to see now what the Middle White might have to offer in the future, but it is surely worth preserving, if only for its amazing appearance and the extent to which it retains the features of its Chinese ancestors.

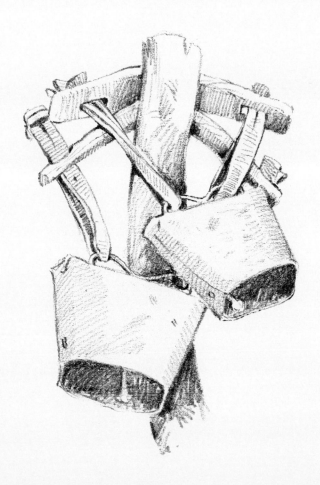

Downland Sheep Farming

The South Downs have always been known as perfect country for sheep. As David Low wrote in the 1840s, 'The herbage of these hills is short, but well adapted for the keeping of Sheep, of which vast numbers have, in every known period, occupied the pastures.' On the lower ground, many of the farms had fields which provided winter fodder for the flocks. In 1830, William Cobbett fondly described the system of downland sheep farming in his *Rural Rides*: 'I like to look at the winding side of a great down with two or three numerous flocks of sheep on it, belonging to different farms; and to see, lower down, the folds in the fields, ready to receive them for the night . . . The sheep principally manure the land. This is to be done by folding . . . Every farm has its portion of down, arable and meadow.'

In this picture are gathered together some of the essentials in the life of a downland shepherd: his dog and his crook, the hut where he lived for the first two months of the year during lambing time, sheep bells and wattle hurdles.

The dog I have shown is like some I have seen in photographs of Sussex shepherds from before World War I. These dogs, which were still used in the 1920s, were not like either the collies that are used as sheepdogs today or the large woolly Old English Sheepdogs that people keep as pets. Their coats were certainly heavy, but rough and serviceable. They were sturdy crossbreeds that were different from modern sheepdogs not only physically but in temperament: because they also had to be guard dogs, they were strong animals perfectly capable of seeing off human intruders. In this, they were perhaps more like the drovers' dogs of the past than the sheepdogs of today.

The head of the crook would have been made by the local blacksmith. Sussex crooks were often superb examples of craftsmanship. The shepherd himself might have suggested one or two small variations on the standard pattern to suit his own preferences. The bells were either made by blacksmiths or bought at sheep fairs. Canister bells, like those in the picture, were the most popular in Sussex, while cluckets, which were also made of folded sheets of metal but were wide at the top and tapered down to the mouth, were more common in Wiltshire. The yokes for the bells were fashioned by the shepherds out of wood cut from the hedges. The leather straps were also made by them, usually from bits of old harness that they cadged from the ploughman who looked after the horses.

The raw material for hurdles came from hazel coppicing, and their production was a woodland industry. The hurdles were used by the shepherds to make folds in which the sheep were enclosed for safety after being brought down off the hills at night. The folds were often placed over mangolds or swedes and moved when necessary as the roots were eaten. The shepherd would carry the hurdles on his back, three or four at a time, to other parts of the field to make another fold.

There were a number of firms that made shepherds' huts, but they tended to conform to the same general pattern. The early ones were made of wood, but some time in the latter part of the nineteenth century, they began to be made of corrugated iron on the outside, usually with a rolled, corrugated iron roof. Inside they were panelled with wood for heat insulation. Beside the door was a stove that provided plenty of warmth for the shepherd who lived there in the coldest part of the year, and at the far end was a bunk bed for him to sleep in.

I found this stockyard near Singleton in Sussex, but the roofs were made of corrugated iron, which I have replaced with peg tiles. I have repaired the fences and added a flock of Southdown sheep being brought out of the stockyard by the shepherd to graze up on the downs all day. The Southdown breed was first developed 200 years ago by John Ellman of Glynde in Sussex from the long-legged, grey-faced sheep that had lived on the downs since time immemorial.

The Southdowns in the drawing are tegs, young sheep before their first
shearing, which I saw at a sale on a Sussex farm. They have the compact
shape, short, broad face and small, rounded ears that are characteristic of
the breed. The colour of the face and legs has been called mouse grey.
Today's Southdowns are smaller than those of Ellman's time, although
French Southdowns are closer to their old size. The breed has contributed
some of its quality to most of the more recent Downs breeds.

Oxford Downs, with their brownish black faces and legs, are the largest of the downland breeds. Some of the sheep bells in my collection are so large that people think they must be cow bells, but sheep like these Oxford Downs would have had no problem in carrying a big canister bell.

Oxford Downs sheltering against a snow-laden hedge. This hardy breed is at home on the exposed arable land of the Cotswolds. It was formed in the middle of the nineteenth century by cross-breeding the Hampshire Down, which was still being developed, with the Cotswold breed, which the Oxford Down largely ousted from its home territory. Today, both the Oxford Down and the Cotswold are minority breeds.

This lambing yard is based on the set-up used near my home in Hertfordshire until recently by my friend Alan Lungley for his flock of Hampshire Downs. He has now changed his system slightly, and his lambing yard is not entirely open, but he is still very much a traditional shepherd. The subject is one that I find quite irresistible – it seems to sum up everything that has fascinated me about the life of the shepherd. Lambing yards like this could have been found almost anywhere on the downlands of southern England for at least the last 200 years.

The construction of the yard is very functional, with the walls all round made into cloisters so that, whichever direction the wind and rain are coming from, there is always protection for the ewes and their lambs. The structure is built of timber, mainly just branches from trees, and thatched with straw. In Sussex, the cloisters would have been given even more warmth and protection from the weather with a covering of gorse, which grew abundantly on the open downs.

I have shown the lambing yard at the end of a January or February day. Light is coming from the hut – at this time of the year, the shepherd would have been in and out all the time to tend his ewes.

One of Alan Lungley's Hampshire Down ewes with a couple of lambs. In the 1830s, Hampshire sheep farmers were experimenting in crossing three breeds from neighbouring counties, the Southdown, the Wiltshire Horn and the Berkshire Nott, a hornless breed with a mottled face, which was said to do well on poor pasture, but has long since become extinct. By this time, the Southdown had been further improved by Jonas Webb of Babraham in Cambridgeshire. The modern Hampshire Down traces its ancestry back to one particular Southdown ram, a son of Webb's renowned ram Babraham, which was bought by William Humfrey of Cold Ash, near Newbury in Berkshire, at the first Royal Show in 1839. The animals bred by Humfrey probably had a higher proportion of Southdown in them than the earlier Hampshire Downs, but the breed is a good example of the way that nineteenth-century sheep breeders based their efforts on crossing the improving breeds such as the Southdown and the Dishley Leicester with animals that had over the centuries adapted themselves to the local conditions. In this way, they improved their stock by building on the strengths of their native breeds.

I have put these Hampshire Down sheep into a setting that is one of my favourites, a Dorset valley not far inland from Bridport, which is one of my richest sources of subject matter. The time is early spring.

Evening on a downland farm at the edge of beech woods in the Chilterns. A few sheep are being driven back along the track to the farm after a day of grazing on the downs.

Animals of the Farm

Even forty years ago, traditional farms had none of the industrial feeling of their modern successors. You can go into a farmyard today when no-one is around and have the feeling of being in the yard of a factory. Gone is the variety of livestock that used to make the farmyard a place with a life of its own. Cattle, sheep and pigs were by no means the only animals that you could expect to find. There would be chickens pecking around in the farmyard and ducks on the pond. Even if the farm no longer used working horses, it would perhaps have had a donkey, and someone around the farm might have had a goat or kept rabbits or geese.

Spotted donkeys, like this one from the local village, are much less common than the ordinary grey-browns. Villagers, particularly women, often had donkey carts, which were used for a variety of purposes.

Donkeys have been in England since Elizabethan times and are the descendants of the African wild ass, which was the earliest of all animals to be domesticated as a beast of burden, probably in the New Stone Age, about 6,000 years ago.

An imaginary farmyard scene into which I have put a couple of our local donkeys. The grey-brown is the mother of the spotted one behind her. I have added a suggestion of my cottage in the background, and some chickens, which would have been free to scratch around, so that they got a good proportion of their food from the farmyard itself. They were not fed all the time, but some corn would have been scattered for them every once in a while.

The goat tethered on a roadside verge or smallholding used to be a common sight. Its value was summed up by a manual on goat-keeping first published in the 1870s: 'The goat has been appropriately termed "The Poor Man's Cow", and certainly no better designation could be found to express the position of this useful creature among our domestic animals. In this respect it may be placed in the same category as the pig, for it converts waste vegetables and other refuse matter into milk as the latter transforms such substances into meat.'

Unlike sheep and cows, goats browse rather than graze and are quite happy nibbling away at all manner of unpromising vegetation – hence their popularity in mountainous countries like Switzerland and in hot, dry places in Greece and Spain, where goats are used for meat and are often the only source of fresh milk. Today, the commercial future of the goat in Britain depends not on the rural poor, but on the foodies who are providing a market for a new generation of country cheeses. My paintings are of Old English, or simply English, goats at the Weald and Downland Museum.

Domesticated rabbits were kept by smallholders and cottagers, either as a source of food or simply as pets. Among the fancy breeds was the English Lop, with its great, Dumbo-like ears which can be as much as 28 inches long and seven inches wide. The two in my pictures belong to my daughters.

During the war, everyone in the village seemed to keep rabbits or chickens, and however cuddly the rabbits might have been, most of them ended up in the pot. I have kept black and white Old English rabbits, like the one at the left of the painting, on and off for forty years. The Old English is one of the breeds intended for meat production. I remember that it was always a hardship for me when one of the rabbits had to go.

A veteran of the farm. This old Fordson tractor, which belongs to a friend, dates from 1937 to 1939. Vintage tractors are now collected by enthusiasts, and early Fordsons like this are very desirable items. This retired tractor, though, has found a place on the farmyard, nicely blocking up an entrance to the straw barn. The chickens, which are enjoying scratching around on it, will use it as a roost later in the evening.

Every farmyard used to have its cat, which helped keep down the mice and rats. This ginger tom is a typical specimen, although the farm cat was just as likely to be black or tabby. Believe it or not, there is such a thing as a working cat. Although cats are by nature predatory, not all of them are hunters like this one. Here he is on the prowl and getting very interested in some rat activity in a dung heap.

Geese in the garden of Thomas Hardy's house, Max Gate.

Geese in a farm setting with a Gloucestershire wagon that I saw at the Cotswold Farm Park.

Ducks on the edge of a pond, an assortment of crossbred birds and, in the foreground of the painting, a Silver Appleyard drake. This is one of the rare breeds that was narrowly saved from extinction.

Rhode Island Red cockerel and hen.

Heavy Horse Breeds

When the horse was first tamed, it was used mainly as a military animal for pulling chariots and later for riding. The more humble domestic tasks of the beast of burden fell to the ox and the ass. In England, the ox remained an important draught animal on farms until the eighteenth century.

The early history of the horse is much more complicated than that of the other farm animals, as it is probably derived from four different wild species that were domesticated at different times and places. The wild ancestor of the heavy horse seems to have been a large animal that lived in marshy areas of Europe such as the Rhine Valley thousands of years ago.

The young grey Shire horse in these studies is beautifully turned out for the Peterborough Heavy Horse Show. A fine pedigree horse like this might have been owned by a well-to-do farmer, who would have had him dressed up and taken to the local shows. This Shire is a young animal with lots of life in him. You have to know what you are doing with heavy horses as large and powerful as this. Luckily, they are willing and docile, because if they decided to act up, they would be very difficult to stop.

Although the Shire may be grey, chestnut or roan as well as black, its ancestor is referred to in some nineteenth-century literature as the Old English Black Horse. It has also in the past been called the Great Horse and the War Horse, which may seem surprising in view of its gentle nature. However, the origins of this breed go back to the late twelfth and early thirteenth centuries, most notably during the reign of King John, when a hundred large stallions were imported from the Low Countries and the banks of the Elbe. The intention was to increase the size and weight of English horses so that they would be better fitted for their main task, which was to carry knights, who weighed as much as 400 pounds in their full armour, into battle.

It was not until the eighteenth century that horses took over from oxen as work animals on farms, and breeders such as Robert Bakewell set out to improve the size and strength of the Old English Black Horse. The modern name of Shire horse comes from the Midland shires where it was bred in the greatest numbers, as Low put it 'from the Humber to the Cam, occupying the rich fens of Lincoln and Cambridge, and extending westward through the counties of Huntingdon, Northampton, Leicester, Nottingham, Derby, Warwick, and Stafford, to the Severn.' The Shire is the largest of the heavy horses and, although it is a slow worker, it has always been valued for its enormous strength.

A fairly young Shire horse, very much like one that I saw on a farm in Yorkshire, where it was just strolling around the yard, looking into the various barns and then clomping off.

Two Suffolk Punches on a farm outside St Albans in Hertfordshire, where the farmer is a respected judge of horses. In the past, the Suffolk Punch was famed for its strength and endurance: many fine horses were ruined in weight-pulling contests in East Anglia. Although the breed is shorter than the Shire, it is almost as heavy because of its stout or punchy shape. The Suffolk Punch is the oldest distinct breed of heavy horse, and every Suffolk is descended through a direct male line from a single stallion, Crisp's Horse, which was foaled in 1768. Another element in its ancestry is the trotting horse, which makes the Suffolk very lively for a heavy horse.

Heavy horse and friend. I found this little scene at a heavy horse centre in Dorset. From time to time, the dove would fly up around the horse and then settle down again. The horse is a grey Clydesdale mare, less usual than black or brown.

The origins of the breed go back to late seventeenth and early eighteenth-century Lanarkshire, where Flemish stallions were used on the native mares, but pedigrees can usually be traced back only to a stallion called Glancer, foaled around 1810. It does not have quite the strength of the Shire or the Suffolk and has finer features. It is inclined to be more nervous than the Shire, but is quicker in action and has a long working life.

Two Suffolk Punch mares. The one on the left is the daughter of the other. The breed has rather short legs, which are clean rather than feathered like those of the Shire or the Clydesdale.

Working Horses

Most of the horses that were in use around the country were very far from being pure-bred. While breeders and rich farmers could take a pride in showing their fine pedigree horses, and industrial firms such as brewers could use a beautifully matched team as part of their image, the vast majority of horses were chosen for much humbler reasons. When I asked our local baker what sort of horses had been used when he was a child, he replied, 'Whatever we could afford that was any good.' And this was probably the principle that was most often behind the choice of a horse.

These studies are all of crossbred horses, although the left-hand pencil drawing shows a heavy horse that is mainly Shire. The others are lighter animals that probably have some Hunter in them. The skill in selecting a working horse was not a matter of looking for the finer points of a particular breed, but of knowing what qualities a horse needed to do the job for which it was intended, which is, after all, the way the breeds came about in the first place. These studies of horses represent exactly the sort of scene that would have been commonplace in the countryside up to World War II, when the internal combustion engine finally took over.

Heavy horses were the tractors of the past, pulling ploughs and big harvest
wagons, and doing any other gruelling jobs of haulage that came up. The
horses in the painting are standing on the headland of a ploughed field at
the end of a day's work. The ploughmen were extremely proud of them,
and, even when working, the horses had their harnesses decorated with
horse brasses. The work of a ploughman must have been extremely hard,
because he had to get up early enough not just to feed the horses, groom
them and tack them up but to give them time to digest their food before
they started work. A good ploughman would not have overworked his
horses, and particularly in winter would have started as early as possible so
that he could take the horses in if the weather turned bad during the day.

This sort of scene of open grazing with a variety of horses and some cattle in the distance would have been common in Hertfordshire and in many other parts of England. That was in the days before so much land was ploughed up to grow cereals. Perhaps now that we are living in the shadow of the grain mountain, we will begin to see more land used for grazing.

Our local baker, John Groom, in Ashridge, where he has delivered bread
ever since he was a boy working with his father. He still has horse-drawn
vehicles, which he sometimes uses for deliveries. He does all his own
baking in a brick oven and has never put any chemicals or additives into
his bread to make it stay artificially fresh – you have to eat it quickly. I
have shown him with the horse that he has now – a tough little cob, just
the sort of animal to be drawing a small delivery cart.

Two crossbred horses at the yard of John, the baker. The gear stacked up against the old gatepost is a typical driving harness for a medium-sized horse. John has vehicles for different purposes: two baker's carts, a dog cart, traps and a dung cart. You have to remember that he has to muck out the stable and do something with the dung, which he certainly is not going to put in the baker's cart. The village people are very happy because he gets rid of his unwanted horse manure by delivering it free of charge.

I have painted this grey mare on Boxmoor in Hertfordshire, where I found her grazing with her foal. She has certainly got some Hunter in her and also some heavy horse – Shire or Clydesdale.

These coloured horses are not, strictly speaking, farm animals. They were much favoured by gipsies who travelled around and worked on farms. As a schoolboy, I used to go pea-picking or spud-hocking – harvesting potatoes – and the gipsies would draw up with their wagons and always with lovely coloured horses. The ones in the picture are crossbreeds, which they probably all would have been, and the horse at the top certainly has a bit of Clydesdale in him.

I found these horses in the West Country with a family of gipsies who have no mechanised transport whatsoever and still live in hoop wagons. They are very knowledgeable about their horses and breed them as they want them, with coloured markings and the right physique for pulling their wagons. It is characteristic of them to plait their horse's mane and tail.

Crossbred cobs like this were the smaller, but still quite strong, general purpose equivalents of the heavy horse. They could pull a cart for deliveries or for taking a pig to market, or a two-seater trap so that you could go off shopping or take a ride on a Sunday. I have put a couple of friends in the trap, and my wife Betty is standing outside our cottage in the background. The dog was owned by our old next-door neighbour, Mr Fowler, who was born in our cottage, as was his father, who had a horse and trap just like the one in the picture. Even now, as you come round the corner, the dog rushes up and down excitedly.

I have painted this small cob rushing off to market with a cart full of freshly cut flowers. The cart is a fine example of the wagonmaker's art, with a lot of skilful chamfering and shaping on the frame. There is a bucket hanging underneath – the first thing the lady will have to do when she gets to market is look after her horse. Only then will she feel free to sell her wares.

Crossbreeds

Just as most working horses were crossbreeds, so were many other farm animals. I am not talking here about such famous crossbreeds as the very prolific Masham and Mule ewes, which are crosses between Swaledale ewes and, respectively, Teeswater and Bluefaced Leicester rams. My subjects on the next few pages are crossbreeds that were much less intentional, but are typical of those that you might have found on a small, mixed farm.

This cockerel is a cross between a Silky and a Buff Orpington. In the background two Rhode Island Reds are rushing off to see what the others in the distance have found to peck at on the ground. The cockerel gets its chestnut colour from the Buff Orpington, and the black as well as the rather crown-like comb and the mottling on the breast are from the Silky. The farmyard is from memory.

This mare is a typical crossbred heavy horse, even though her colour is striking – completely white except for her head, which looks as if someone has tipped soot over it. I found her leaning against an old willow tree on Halvergate Marshes in Norfolk, which are full of grazing animals. You never know what you are going to come across: you can see Highland cattle one minute and Belted Galloways the next.

I found this character in Cambridgeshire. Its parents were both Middle Whites of the standard pinkish colour, but their offspring was covered in big black blotches. The farmer said that one of its grandparents must have been a Large Black, and I think he was right. I have chosen this setting because pigs love woodlands. However domesticated they are, you have only to give them an opportunity to run in the woods and they will mooch around happily.

The same crossbred Middle White in a pose that I could not resist, clearly wondering whether it can manage to wedge down one or two more turnips.

Chickens

The chickens that I have painted for this book are all farmyard breeds: big, robust birds whose lives make those of today's free-range chickens look pathetically restricted. You would hardly recognise them as being the same species as the pathetic broilers and egg-machines that are the inmates of the poultry industry's indoor concentration camps. You can appreciate by looking at them that these could be the descendants of birds that lived in the wild. The ancestors of the modern chicken were probably the Red Jungle Fowl of India and south-east Asia. Domestic chickens were imported into Britain in the first century AD.

This Buff Orpington cockerel is perched conspicuously on a fence, as high as he can get, dominating the area around him and crowing his head off in the early morning light. Like most of the breeds of poultry that we think of as traditional, the Buff Orpington has been around for less than a century. Chicken breeds can be developed and then lost so quickly that a poultry expert of a hundred years ago would not recognise the majority of our best known breeds, while those he favoured have either vanished or are near extinction.

The Buff Orpington was launched as a breed in 1894 by William Cook of Orpington in Kent, who eight years earlier had had a big success with the Black Orpington, which was described in a poultry book as 'a large, useful fowl, specially suitable for residents in towns and manufacturing districts'. Cook claimed that the Black Orpington was developed from three other breeds, the Black Minorca, Black Plymouth Rock and Clean-legged Langshan. His published recipe for the Buff Orpington involved three other breeds, the Buff Cochin, Dark Dorking and Gold-spangled Hamburgh.

Something very similar, however, had been around for at least twenty years previously in the Spalding area under the name of Lincolnshire Buff. To make matters even more confusing, Lincolnshire breeders claimed a somewhat different origin for their concoction, which was supposed to be a mixture of Buff Cochin, Dorking and Common Fowl. There were also White and Spangled Orpingtons, each said to have a different ancestry.

Disputes like this made tempers run high in the world of turn-of-the-century chicken fanciers. A contributor to *Feathered World* on 16th December 1898 fulminated, ' . . . when a man has already appropriated the name of his own residence to one breed, of which he tells us the components were A, B, and C, there are the gravest objections to his giving, years afterwards, the same name, for merely trade and advertising purposes, to another "breed," which, according to his own account, has no particle of A, B, and C, but was built up of X, Y, Z.'

However, even if it was no more than an improved Lincolnshire Buff, the Buff Orpington was such a valuable breed, being tasty to eat and obligingly producing buff-shelled eggs, that anything roughly the right colour was sold as a Buff Orpington. A Lincolnshire breeder wrote, 'If I call my birds Lincolnshire Buff, I cannot get more than 4s. each for them; if I call them Buff Orpington, they sell readily at 10s. each.'

Like many a fashion, the Buff Orpington was heavily overpublicised: 'If one tithe of what has been said respecting them were true, they would deserve to be canonized,' wrote one expert. Nevertheless, the Buff Orpington remained popular in the twentieth century. The hen in the picture has a mixture of chicks that she has hatched out. The chicken coop, which is my own, is literally just a nesting box. If anything alarms the hen, she will shuffle back into it and the chicks will follow.

The Brahma cockerel is very tall in the painting because he is protecting the hens and attacking me, coming backwards at me with his spurs, which are hidden by the feathers down the outside of his legs. Brahma is an abbreviation of Brahmaputra, and the breed is said to have originated in India, but was imported into America and developed in Connecticut. The first birds to arrive in Britain were sent to Queen Victoria by a New England breeder said to be 'pushing the breed for all it was worth.'

The number of poultry varieties is greatly increased by the fact that each colour variation has a status of its own. At the beginning of this century, the Sussex Poultry Club recognised three colours, the Red or Brown Sussex, the Speckled Sussex and the Light Sussex. Some breeders, though, regarded only the first two as true Sussexes. Nevertheless, it is the Light Sussex that has been the most successful.

Sussex chickens were being referred to in the early 1800s, but did not come into their own as a breed until the end of the century. They were overshadowed by the closely related Dorkings, which breeders had started promoting in the 1850s. The original difference between the two breeds seems to have been that the Dorking had five claws while the Sussex had four. Both seem to have been thought of as particularly delicious.

The colour of the Light Sussex makes it very satisfying to paint. Birds like these do not fit into the horrible battery chicken business. Now that everyone is wanting free-range eggs, perhaps we will see a variety of breeds coming back again. The medical profession says that we should not eat more than three eggs a week, so perhaps we can spend our money on three eggs with some taste rather than having six from poor birds that have been fed on chemicals and kept in a prison.

Pure-bred Rhode Island Reds entering the stubble to glean among the
stooks in the harvest field. This is one of the most popular breeds and
seemed to be the one that everybody had in the back yard during the war:
you might call it America's most charming contribution to the war effort.
The breed seems to have been developed in New England in the 1880s,
and its ancestry included local breeds and birds brought from Asia by sea
captains. At the beginning of this century, it was almost unknown in Europe.

Variety

After World War II, farming became ever more intensive. All the pressures on farmers led towards an increasingly dreary and even dangerous uniformity. Britain's wealth of regional breeds that had been evolved to thrive in their various environments came to seem less and less relevant to current needs. After all, when animals are being kept in factory conditions, it makes little difference to them where the factory is located. So the natural tendency was to find which sort worked best and then stick with it. As a result, more than 90 per cent of our milk comes from Friesians, and 90 per cent of British pigs are Large Whites or Landraces or a mixture of the two.

It is perhaps because sheep are not very susceptible to being raised intensively that Britain still has 52 breeds of sheep, as against 29 of cattle and eleven of pigs. The routine availability of artificial insemination for cattle and pigs, though not for sheep, has been another major factor in promoting uniformity. When a single bull can provide up to 80,000 artificial inseminations in a year, the most popular breeds can be available to almost every farmer as herd sires. In one year during the 1970s, Friesians accounted for 93 per cent of the artificial inseminations of dairy and dual-purpose cattle under the auspices of the Milk Marketing Board. On the other hand, the Rare Breeds Survival Trust has used artificial insemination as an aid to conservation.

The Lincoln Longwool is our largest breed of sheep and evolved over hundreds of years in its native country. It was used by Robert Bakewell two hundred years ago in the development of his Dishley Leicester breed, which in turn was used to improve the Lincoln. In the 1840s, David Low, who considered what he called the Old Lincoln Breed 'the most remarkable breed of Sheep which the British Isles have produced,' expressed regret that it 'had not rather been improved by an application of the principle of selection, than destroyed in its distinctive characters by indiscriminate crossing.' The same comment could have been made on many other occasions about numerous other breeds, up to the present day.

Even so, today's Lincoln Longwool has retained many of the qualities of the Old Lincoln, including its hardiness. It is able to live on marshy land, and, with its coat of up to fifteen pounds of wool, it is well equipped to withstand the bitter east winds that come in off the North Sea. Lincoln wool is in demand for its length and lustre, and the skins make fine sheepskin rugs.

I have painted these Lincoln Longwools without their full coat of long, hanging curls. At this point, you can see their faces before the curls grow to cover everything.

The Hereford bull belongs to a breed that is anything but rare. Indeed, the Hereford has been Britain's most important beef breed during this century, although it has not achieved the same level of dominance as the Friesian has among dairy cattle, and its position has been eroded in the past twenty years by the fashion for importing such alien breeds as the Charolais, Limousin, Simmental and Murray Grey.

The white head that is the hallmark of the breed was not a constant feature until the nineteenth century, but is of much earlier origin. It is said to have come from Dutch stock imported around 1650 by Lord Scudamore and crossed with the red cattle that were then found in the Midlands and along the Welsh borders. Herefordshire was already renowned for its cattle in the seventeenth century, and the breed was further improved in the eighteenth by Benjamin Tomkins and others. Their intention was to produce large, heavy cattle that could be used as draught animals for ploughing and then, at the age of about six, could be sold at a good price to Midland graziers to be fattened up for beef.

With its red colour and white head and underparts, the Hereford is instantly recognisable. It is able to do well in all sorts of conditions and is to be found in great numbers throughout the cattle-producing areas of the world, from Canada to Australia and South Africa. In the United States, it even replaced the Texas Longhorn on the ranches of the southwestern states.

What appeals to me in these Dairy Shorthorns is their colour, which varies from red to white through a variety of roans and brindles. This herd, which I found near Leighton Buzzard in Buckinghamshire, did not have horns, and so I have had to put these back.

The Shorthorn was developed by the Colling brothers around 1800, primarily as a beef animal, from the old Teeswater breed of north Yorkshire, but some strains retained their milking qualities. The Dairy Shorthorn is a dual-purpose breed that has fallen from favour in recent years because it is no rival for the Friesian in producing vast amounts of milk.

Galloways are descended from the black cattle that were found on the western side of Britain. The distinguishing feature of these Belted Galloways may have come from crossing with Lakenvelder cattle from Holland, which are similarly marked. All the Galloway breeds are hardy animals with a dense undercoat beneath their long hair to protect them from the elements on the exposed hillsides of their native area. It is said that polled (hornless) strains were selected by breeders to save drovers from horn injuries. From the seventeenth century until the arrival of railways in the nineteenth, anything up to 30,000 cattle a year travelled down the drove roads from southern Scotland. Low wrote in the 1840s, 'They are reared to the age of two or three years on the farms of the country, and are driven southward, mostly in the latter part of the season, and chiefly to the counties of Norfolk and Suffolk. They are purchased by English graziers, wintered on straw, hay, and green food, and fattened on the grass of the following season, and driven to Smithfield, supplying a large part of the consumption of the city from Christmas to July.'

131

You have only to look at this Highland bull to realise what a hardy beast he is. Descended from the animals that have lived for many hundreds of years in the Highlands and the Hebrides, the breed can survive in conditions that no other would tolerate and exist off the sparsest of grazing.

Today's Highland cattle are a mixture of the old Kyloe cattle of the Hebrides, which were small, shaggy and usually black, with mainland stock of various colours. As attempts to 'improve' them by crossing with larger, fleshier breeds would inevitably have resulted in a loss of hardiness, they are perhaps the nearest thing that we have to the partly domesticated cattle of Neolithic times. On the other hand, they have been used in the development of some other breeds, including the Shorthorn. Low mentions that, 'In some of the few remaining pine forests of the north of Scotland, cows which are left to stray become as wild as deer, and are shot in the same manner.'

In the eighteenth century, Highland cattle were brought south by the drovers, and were highly valued by English dealers. Although Highland cattle can be seen in the south, it is in the most rugged parts of Scotland that the pure-bred Highland has been, and probably always will be, able to hold its own against all comers.

The eye and the shape of the horns were enough to make me want to paint a close-up of this English billy goat. Although the English goat is not classed as rare, the goat now plays such a small part in our rural economy that no breed is really common.

These kids are Golden Guernseys. It is a matter of discussion what stock
the breed was developed from and how long it has been in existence.
Certainly, though, it only survived the German occupation of Guernsey
during World War II thanks to a single breeder, Miss Milbourne, who
apparently managed to keep some animals hidden away in caves. There are
now a few hundred of them, in Britain as well as in Guernsey, but they are
still considered a rare breed.

Although many of the animals I have painted belong to rare breeds, this book is not meant simply as a plea for their preservation. Remarkable as some of them are, their survival is only one element in saving the countryside as a whole, though it is obviously better that these animals should survive in farm parks and countryside museums than become extinct. With so much of our farm land, as well as the animals, plants and buildings on it, reduced to a state of miserable uniformity, it is essential that we should not lose any more of the richness of variety that gave the English farm much of its character and resilience. The mixed farm deserves more than to become grist to the mill of the nostalgia industry.

My last painting represents the one thing that we must all remember as we are leaving wherever we have been in the countryside.

Pictures

All the pictures were specially painted or drawn for this book, except for the frontispiece, which belongs to the Weald & Downland Museum, Singleton, near Chichester, Sussex.